THE SHOWN SERIES

Edited by Louey Chisholm

NESTS AND EGGS

NESTS AND EGGS

by

A. H. BLAIKIE

described by

J. A. HENDERSON

Forty-eight coloured pictures

THOMAS NELSON AND SONS LTD
LONDON EDINBURGH PARIS MELBOURNE
TORONTO AND NEW YORK

THOMAS NELSON AND SONS LTD

Parkside Works Edinburgh 9
3 Henrietta Street London WC2
312 Flinders Street Melbourne C1
5 Parker's Buildings Burg Street Cape Town

THOMAS NELSON AND SONS (CANADA) LTD
91–93 Wellington Street West Toronto 1

THOMAS NELSON AND SONS
385 Madison Avenue New York 17

SOCIÉTÉ FRANÇAISE D'EDITIONS NELSON
25 rue Henri Barbusse Paris V^e

TO

JOHN FRANCIS SANDARS

ABOUT NESTS AND EGGS

IT is probable that many hundreds of years ago all birds' eggs were white. Very slowly, through long stretches of time, they have been modified to suit their different conditions, until now they show a large variety of colouring. And we may take it, too, that when birds first began to be, there was none of the dainty nest-building with which we are so familiar. That took some time to invent and to learn. And the earliest birds' eggs were laid on or in the ground. Very gradually birds have adapted their habits to the conditions in which they have found themselves, so that as much variety is now to be found among their dwelling-places as among those of men. The simple requirements of one bird are satisfied by a hole in the ground, as she may rear her young on a bare rock quite unsheltered from the weather. Another builds an elaborate home, hanging it up among the leaves of a tree, in a bag made of two of these leaves sewn together. And the bower-birds make not only houses, but stately pleasure-grounds as well; lay out gardens and build bowers where they play, and decorate them daily with fresh flowers.

Among the homes of our native birds, these pictures will show you that the variety is very great. The Shearwater lays her egg in a bare hole dug in peat; the Sand-martin lines with straw the hole she makes in the sand; and the Kingfisher gradually amasses fish-bones for a bed in her hole in the river-bank. The Bottle-tit brings a wonder of care and ingenuity to the making of her home; the Ring-dove's nest is just the least that will hold together in the tree. The Moorhen says "No trouble is too great," and builds fresh nest after nest as her growing family requires; the Partridge says "In a safe place, anything will do," and makes her nest by turning round and round in a clump of grass till it is trodden down in the centre; while the Cuckoo finds some one else to build for her and to tend her young as well. One bird chooses clay as a likely material for comfort; another prefers cobwebs, and another feathers and down. One will use broken shells and another brown slimy seaweed. Each bird selects the site for his home according to where he can find the kind of food he needs, and the kind of nest he builds depends on the position chosen. In every case that kind is used that the experience and discretion of previous generations have commended as being best protected from the natural enemies likely to be found in its particular surroundings.

Wherever the eggs are laid they are of an appropriate shape. In the deep nests out of which they cannot roll, they are more round in form than those that lie on the bare ground. Where they are exposed to gales on a cliff-edge, their shape is such that they do not roll off, but merely turn round and round in the wind. The Sand-piper's eggs have pointed ends; they are so large that if they could not be packed closely together, the bird could not cover them to keep them warm, and so the chicks inside would die.

And according to where they lie, the colouring, too, is modified for their protection. The eggs of the Green Plover are of mottled colours in harmony with the grass and heather among which they are laid, their dull green or brown covered and broken up with dark markings; and the young chicks are equally difficult to see when they squat flat on the ground and lie motionless. The Ringed Plover's eggs lie on the seashore, so they are sandy or grey stone-coloured; their markings are not blots and splashes of dark colours, but small spots and speckles, which are much less visible against the broken shells and gravel. The eggs that are hidden in holes in the ground or in deep nests need no protective colours; the Dipper's eggs are white and the Kingfisher's shining white. The Duck's light-coloured eggs that she must cover up to protect them from cold when she leaves them, are protected at the same time from sight.

With all our birds we can find instinctive habits prompted directly by some device of Nature for their protection. A bird does a particular thing in a particular way, by instinct; but somewhere there is a reason for his way of doing it, for that instinct is the accumulated experience of all the generations of his forefathers. And it is this evidence of a cause for every detail that makes the real interest in the study of nests and eggs. A mere collection of faded eggs, lying in a drawer with labels on them, is not a very interesting thing; and the getting of it together is inevitably fraught with some suffering to the birds, for of course their loss is far greater than the collector's gain. But an egg in its natural surroundings gains so much from all it stands for, that it is not only intensely interesting, but far more beautiful too. And there is a whole life, with all its incidents and interests, to follow from it, and another voice to gladden the hills.

J. A. HENDERSON.

LIST OF PLATES

NESTS AND EGGS

THE MISSEL-THRUSH

THE Missel-thrush sets to work about his nest very early in the year. He sometimes finds his mate even so early as January, and by the end of February their house-building may be well under way. As theirs is a large nest, set in the fork of a tree whose leaves have not yet begun to appear, it is very easily seen. And the nest is shallow in form, more like a saucer than a cup, so that the bird sitting on it is not much hidden from view. The nest is made of twigs, dry grasses, wool and lichens. Some mud is worked into it, which helps very much in fixing it firmly to the bark of the tree, and particularly in stiffening and forming the bed. The inside is then lined with fine grasses.

The four or five eggs are laid in March. They are bluish or greenish white, spotted and blotched all over with dark reddish brown and paler shades of grey and lilac. The Missel-thrush often rears two broods in a season.

THE SONG-THRUSH

IT must be a very difficult thing to build a nest of any kind, and must need much skill and patience. But that of the Song-thrush is surely one of the cleverest and most difficult. The outside of it is thick and is made of grasses and moss and fine twigs. For the inside lining there is a firm wall, which is beautifully round and as smooth as the inside walls of our houses. The bird makes the plaster for this of clay and wet mud, with scraps of all sorts of soft things, such as decayed wood, to bind it. Then she moulds the cup by moving round and round in it, pressing the damp sides of it with her breast. And when the plaster dries it is all round and smooth, and so strong that it often lasts long after the outer part of the nest has been torn to pieces by the wild winds in autumn.

This wonderful home is generally built in a thick bush or hedge or among ivy growing against a wall. In it are laid four, five, or six eggs of a strong clear blue, with spots of black. Two or three families are reared each season, the first chicks being hatched in April.

THE BLACKBIRD

THE Blackbird's nest may be seen in the same sort of position as the Song-thrush chooses—in the middle of a hedge or in a thornbush or an evergreen, or in ivy growing against a tree or wall. It is generally three or four feet from the ground, but is sometimes hidden in a hole in a bank or wall. It is like the Throstle's on the outside, as he uses much the same kinds of material—small twigs and roots and stems, mixed with grasses and moss. He, too, uses wet clay to strengthen the frame, mixing it in with his other materials to cement them together and to form the centre. He finishes the inside differently, however, with a thick warm lining of the finest grasses mixed with horse-hair.

The building is begun in March, and the first brood of chicks are out of the nest by the end of April or the beginning of May. Another clutch of eggs is laid in a new nest, and after that a third. The eggs are about five in number, and of a dull greenish blue, mottled and spotted with greenish brown.

Missel-Thrush (see Plate XXXVII.)
Song-Thrush (see Plate XXXVII.)

PLATE II

Blackbird (see Plate XXXVII.)

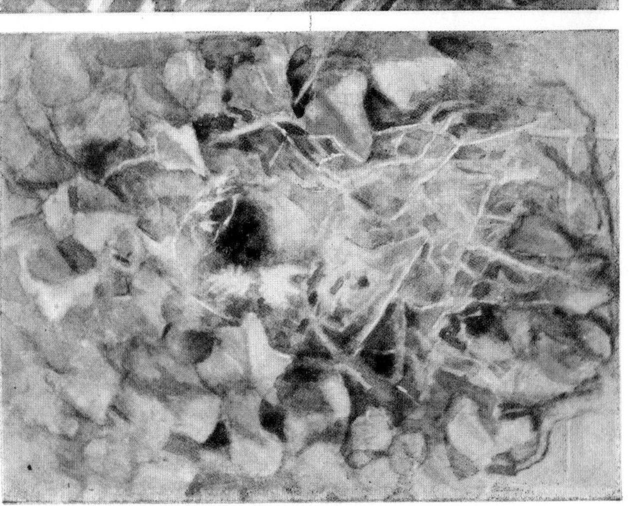

House-Sparrow (see Plate XXXVII.)

THE HOUSE SPARROW

THIS is the most familiar to us of all birds' nests, for the Sparrow's favourite position for his nest is in some hole or corner about our houses. And he is such an untidy, careless fellow that straws dangling clumsily from it generally show where he has taken up his abode. Sparrows are so noisy too, always chattering and scolding, that you need never be at a loss as to their whereabouts. When there is no suitable corner to be had about a house, the nest is built in a tree; and then it is that you can see its proper form. It is a domed nest; that is a nest with a roof, and having its opening at the side. It is made of dry grasses, straws, wool, or any suitable thing to be found, and lined with feathers.

The eggs are greyish white, shaded with darker grey and spotted with black. About five eggs are laid, and as soon as the chicks are independent, another clutch, and another, from February or March right on till September or October.

The Sparrow often takes possession of the neat nest of a Swallow or House-martin, turning the builders of it out of their rightful home.

THE CHAFFINCH

IN the fork of a low bush or tree you may often find the home of the Chaffinch, or often in an old thorn hedge by the roadside. Perhaps the bush or thorn is covered with white or grey lichen; then the Chaffinch carefully weaves scraps of the lichen into her nest along with the green moss and wool, making it so like its surroundings that the eye does not readily distinguish it. It is a very neat little nest that she makes and very compact. The materials are so cleverly felted together that while it looks slight it is amply strong and snug. The deep cup of it is lined with hair and feathers, and that makes it a very comfortable home.

The eggs are laid in April or May, four, five, or six in number. They are of a dull bluish white, marked with reddish and dark reddish brown. The "Shilfa," as the Chaffinch is often called, is a very brave and faithful mother, and will sometimes allow herself to be taken in the hand rather than leave her nestlings. Like all the finches the Chaffinch generally rears two broods in a season.

THE GREENFINCH

ALTHOUGH it is not nearly so neat as that of the Chaffinch, the nest of the Greenfinch certainly looks comfortable, does it not? It is a much bigger nest, to begin with. Then the birds have used mosses, and wool, and down, and feathers worked in among some rather coarse grasses; and it is all loose and soft and downy, with the down and feathers sticking out all over it.

The little centre part, however, is quite firm. The hairs and small fibrous roots of the lining are more tightly blended and arranged than are the materials of the outer walls.

A curious thing is that while most birds prefer to have their nests away from neighbours, the Greenfinch is more sociable, and you may sometimes find, close together, the nests of two or three pairs. They build in an evergreen or other bush, or in a hedge or tree, and the first eggs appear early in April. They are dull white or bluish white, decorated at the big end with spots of red-brown, and there are five or six in a clutch.

PLATES IV and XXXVII

THE BULLFINCH

THERE is something of elegance and beauty about the Bullfinch that no other bird of his family can rival. He is aristocratic in all he does. He prefers for his food the exquisite buds of fruit-blossoms, surely a dainty taste. And while fruit-growers hate him for a thief who can in a very short time blight the hopes from a whole orchard, one feels that at least he is a gentleman-highwayman. He is never commonplace. The mere fact that he alone of the Finches mates for life sets him apart a little and appeals to our sentiment. Like everything else about him, his nest is delightful. It has a certain air of distinction, and it is made on a pattern of his own. First comes a broad, flat foundation of roots and twigs, very slight and dainty; and in the centre of this the shallow cup has its rim standing above the platform, and is made of finest root-fibres and horse-hair closely woven.

This nest is to be found often in a yew or some other evergreen, or in a close thorn-hedge. The four or five pale blue eggs are spotted with brown and black.

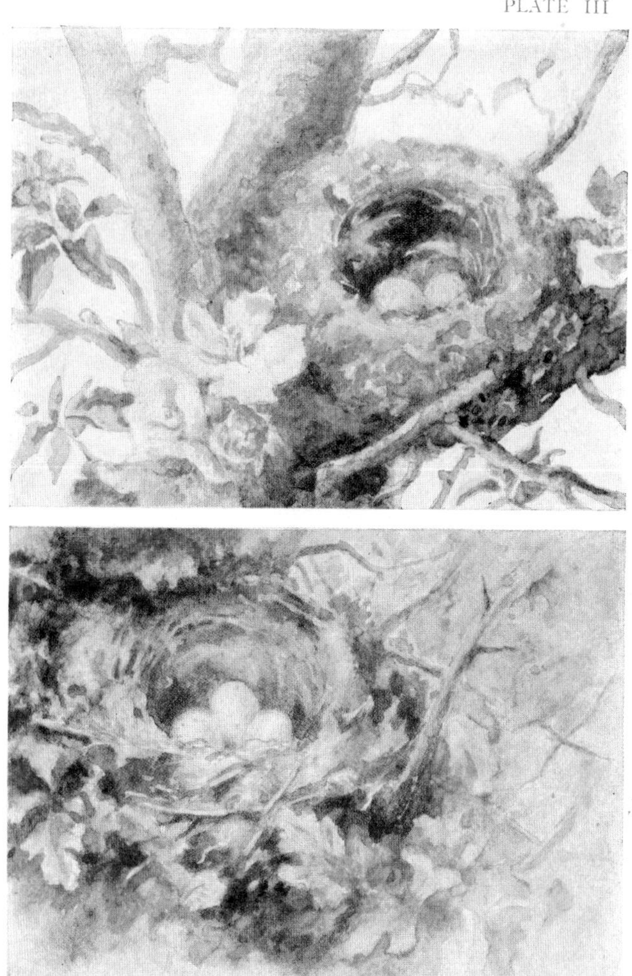

Chaffinch (see Plate XXXVII.)
Greenfinch (see Plate XXXVII.)

PLATE IV

Bullfinch (see Plate XXXVII.)
Goldfinch (see Plate XXXVII.)

THE GOLDFINCH

THE Goldfinch is very often associated in our minds with thistle-down. Certainly a patch of fluffy thistle-tops must suggest the Goldfinch to any one who has watched this gay person in his favourite surroundings. And thistle-down is just what his nest suggests, too! Looking at it from above, when you see the shallow, soft-lined cup, it seems downy and fragile. But it is very beautifully and carefully woven. The outside is of fine roots and twigs, lichens and grasses, and the lining of wool, feathers or vegetable down woven together with horse-hair.

The Goldfinch is singularly fearless when he is building, and often chooses the situation for his nest in a garden or park, even where people keep passing near it. He builds in the fork of a tree, often quite high up. It may be in an oak or a beech, but very often he prefers a fruit-tree; or he will build in a low bush or hedge. The eggs are five or six in number, pale bluish or greenish white, spotted round the larger end with reddish brown.

THE LINNET

THE Linnet lives most on open downs or commons, and as you would therefore expect, the nest is oftenest to be found in gorse or other low bushes. Sometimes it may be in a blackthorn or some such higher tree, but it is very seldom more than a few feet from the ground. It is often on the ground, in a thick tussock, under some protecting shrub. The materials used in building are dry grasses and small twigs, root fibres and moss. The nest is lined with wool and hair and sometimes feathers, and vegetable down such as willow catkins afford.

About the end of April the Linnet lays her first nestful of eggs. They are four, five or six in number, of the palest possible shade of blue, almost white. They are marked principally at the larger end with dark brownish red or purple spots. Two broods are generally reared in the season, the first chicks being ready to fly about the end of May.

THE WHITETHROAT

ANOTHER nest to be sought for in furze or other low vegetation is the slender home of the Whitethroat. It may be in a straggling bramble thicket, or low down in a thick hedge; or, remembering that another name for the Whitethroat is Nettle-creeper, you will look for it and sometimes find it among those dangerous tangles where nettles grow. It is not always carefully hidden, so it is not a very difficult nest to find. It is made of dry grasses, stems and bents, with horse-hair and some down. Sometimes when it is among gorse, scraps of the stems and woolly seed-pods are worked in. It is very loosely put together and so thin and fragile that it is almost surprising that it should hold a whole family. In some cases the same position is used for several years.

The Whitethroat lays four or five eggs, of a pale greenish or greyish white, speckled with grey-green and pale brown.

THE ROBIN

THE Robin usually builds his nest near the ground, often in a hole in a bank or in a wall; sometimes it is in some thick low bush or hedge, and ivy growing against a wall affords another favourite position. It is generally very carefully and cleverly hidden, and the birds are particularly shy of intruders. But in nest-building, as in all his other affairs, the Robin sometimes shows surprising confidence in mankind. What wins our affection always is his frank response to any sympathy or kindness shown by us; and his way of demanding and expecting good feeling must surely secure it for him often. At any rate, he more often than most birds will build in any convenient corner about a human habitation, in a box put out for him, in a corner in the porch, or even inside the house of some tried friend.

Dead leaves are principally used to make the nest, with mosses and fine stalks, and it is lined with hair and wool and some feathers. The eggs are white, tinged with pale grey or often with palest red, and they are generally speckled with light red, though quite frequently they are found pure white and unspotted. There are five or six in a clutch, and two or three broods are reared

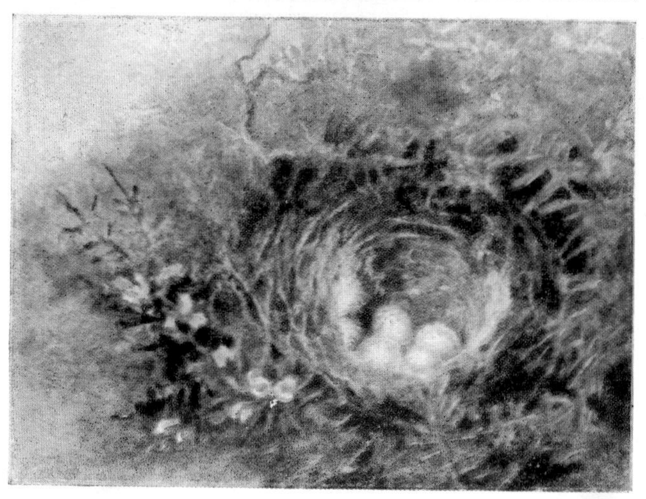

Whitethroat (see Plate XXXVII.)
Linnet (see Plate XXXVII.)

PLATE VI

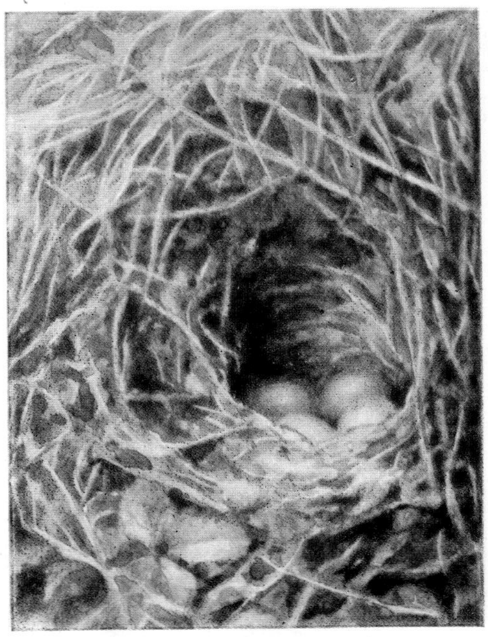

Robin (see Plate XXXVIII.)

Nightingale (see Plate XXXVIII.)

in the season. Robins begin building early in the year, and the eggs are often laid by the beginning of April.

PLATES VI and XXXVIII

THE NIGHTINGALE

THE Nightingale arrives in this country in April, and chooses for his summer quarters some small wood or copse, or a park or shrubbery. He generally prefers to be near a lake or running water. He is not a timid bird, and you may come quite close to him while he sings, as he does at all hours of the twenty-four. The nest, which is rather roughly and loosely put together, is of dried leaves and grasses, with finer grasses and root fibres more compactly woven for the lining. It is placed on the ground among ferns or tall grass and undergrowth, or under some hedge whose straggling branches protect it.

The Nightingale lays five or six eggs of a deep olive-brown colour. They have a smooth, glossy surface, and are not marked or spotted at all. They are laid in May, and about the middle of June the young birds are hatched. Then the parents' time is entirely occupied in attending to their wants, and the singing is over for the summer.

THE WILLOW-WARBLER

THE nest of the Willow-warbler or Willow-wren has more form and depth than have many of the ground nests, and must need greater skill in the building than some of the others. For it is compact and round, with a dome or roof covering it, and its doorway at the side. It is rather large, considering the tiny size of the builders. The materials used are fine dry grasses, fine root fibres and moss, with some dead leaves or ferns; and for the inside of this delightful nursery, first horse-hair and then lots of feathers.

It is almost always placed on the ground, in a hole under a tussock of coarse grass, or under a hedge or bush, or where it is sheltered and hidden by ferns or other low herbage.

The eggs vary a good deal in marking and in number. There are from four to eight of them, and they are tiny, fragile things with a white shell so delicate that the yolk shows through it and gives it a pink tinge. They are generally covered more or less with fine speckles of pale brown or rusty red, but have sometimes very little marking and sometimes none at all. Like many of the eggs that are laid in deep nests, they are round in form.

PLATES VII and XXXVIII

THE SEDGE-WARBLER

OF course no one need be told where to look for the Sedgebird. His name calls up visions of lakes and broads, marshes and slow-running rivers, wherever flags and rushes grow. And to any one who knows this small songster, these memories are associated with his constant churr and chatter that one gradually learns to count among the most pleasing of spring songs. From the eagerness of his singing, that goes on day and night, even when heavy, damp mists hang over his home, from the eagerness of all his movements one pictures him quick and eager in his building. The nest is made among his sedgy, water-side haunts, in a low willow or alder, or on the ground among coarse grass or reeds. It is made of dry stems from the tough grasses around, with some moss and leaves; fine grasses and hair are used for the inside.

Early in May five eggs are laid, of a dull grey brown, marked all over with speckles of yellowish brown, and with a few blackish streaks on the larger end. The hen sits very close, but when the nest is approached too near both birds show their agitation by their quick, anxious movements near it.

THE HEDGE-SPARROW

THIS bird begins her year's work very early. She has much to get through in the season, for she always rears two broods and often even a third. Early in March her neat nest is built in a thorn or any other low bush or hedge. Often it is to be found in ivy that grows against a wall. It is never more than a few feet from the ground. In form it is round and deep, and it is deftly woven of straw, grasses, moss and wool, hair and wool being used to line it.

"The blue of a Hedge-sparrow's egg" is a phrase often used, and so familiar that many people know what a Hedge-sparrow's egg is like who have never thought of wondering about the eggs of any other bird. The phrase describes a delicate shade of greenish blue, very clear and beautiful. Four or five eggs are laid before the end of March.

PLATE VII

Willow-Warbler (see Plate XXXVIII.)

Sedge Warbler (see Plate XXXVIII.)

PLATE VIII

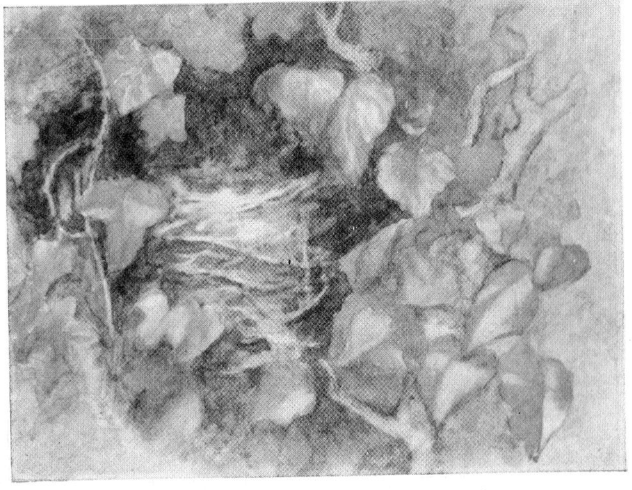

Hedge-Sparrow (see Plate XXXVIII.)
Spotted Flycatcher (see Plate XXXVIII.)

THE SPOTTED FLYCATCHER

THE Flycatcher is a late migrant to this country. Living on insects as he does, of course he cannot come here till the weather is warm enough to bring out his prey. So he does not arrive till about the middle of May.

In all his household affairs the Flycatcher allows himself a wide choice. The position for his nest is oftenest in a tree or ivy growing against a wall; but it may be on the branches of a tree; in a corner of a trellis or a hole in a wall; on the half-open door of an outhouse even, or on a cross-beam in a barn or shed. In fact, any corner that affords a sufficient resting-place is made to serve.

In the things used in building, these birds are equally wide in their tastes; fine grass, feathers, rootlets, moss and hair do duty, the finer materials woven into an inner lining.

The eggs vary in number from four to six; and also in colour, for they are sometimes bluish white and sometimes palest green. They are clouded and blotched with light red and purplish tones.

THE WREN

THE nest of the Wren is oftenest to be found in woods, about the roots or trunks of old dead trees, or among piles of dry brushwood. It is generally close to the ground, sometimes in a hole in a bank or wall, sometimes in the narrow space between a wall and the trunk of a climbing tree; occasionally so high as the thatch of a cottage or the top of a haystack, where she makes a hole for herself.

The hen does all the building, while the cock brings her the fine twigs, dry leaves, ferns, mosses and straws she requires; and for the lining finer mosses and feathers. It is a loosely-built house that she makes, but with a sound framework, and so arranged that the floor, that is to carry the weight, and the entrance where there is to be so much traffic, are the strongest parts. It is dome-shaped, with the door at the side; large for the size of the bird, but not too big a nursery for the seven or eight chicks that are to occupy it.

The Wren will readily leave a nest if she is disturbed in the construction of it, so that half-built nests are often found. The eggs are white with the faintest brownish tinge, and speckled round the larger end with reddish brown.

PLATES IX and XL

THE CUCKOO

NO one quite knows what are the Cuckoo's motives for her strange custom of building no nest, but leaving her eggs and young ones to the care of some other bird. Does she do this to ensure that her young shall have care and attention up to the time when they are able to start for the south in September? For the old birds leave this country in the middle of August, before the young are strong enough for the journey. And the Cuckoo does not put her egg into the nests of other early migrants, such as the Swift. She certainly has some reason other than carelessness, for she has been observed to watch at a distance; and even, where a foster-mother has been killed, the Cuckoo has been known to feed her own chick attentively.

The nests she chooses to leave her egg in are most often those of the Meadow-pipit, Water-wagtail, and Hedge-sparrow; but it is also found in many others. The Cuckoo's egg is a very small one for her size, so that it does not look very different from those it is placed beside, although it is the egg of a very much bigger bird. When the young bird is hatched he grows very quickly, and he is able when only two or three days old to lift on his back and throw out of the nest the other eggs or nestlings he finds beside him.

The egg varies in colour a good deal, sometimes being more or less like those it is left with. Generally it is dull greenish or reddish grey, very much clouded and spotted, especially at the larger end, with dark grey and reddish brown.

THE NUTHATCH

THE Nuthatch is a tree bird only; he lives on the trees, finds his food on the trees, and makes his home right inside a tree. He chooses one where a hole has been caused by the decaying of the wood, either high up in the trunk or in a thick branch. Using his strong beak as a pick-axe, he breaks away the rotten wood and removes it, until the hole is big enough for a comfortable nest. And where the entrance is too big he builds it up with clay until it is just large enough to let him come and go easily. The clay is made rough on the outside so that it may show as little as possible against the bark of the tree.

Having made the place ready for the nest the birds then collect in it dried leaves, moss, or pieces of thin, flaky bark and the thin wings and scales of the pine-cone. These lie un-arranged in the bottom of the hole, making a soft lining.

This nest-building is begun at the end of March, and the five, six, or seven eggs are laid in April. They are clear white, neatly speckled with dark brownish red or brownish purple. The Nuthatch defends her eggs and young ones bravely, hissing at any intruder, and attacking him with her strong bill.

Wren (see Plate XXXVIII.)

Young Cuckoo in Meadow-pipit's Nest
(see Plate XL.)

PLATE X

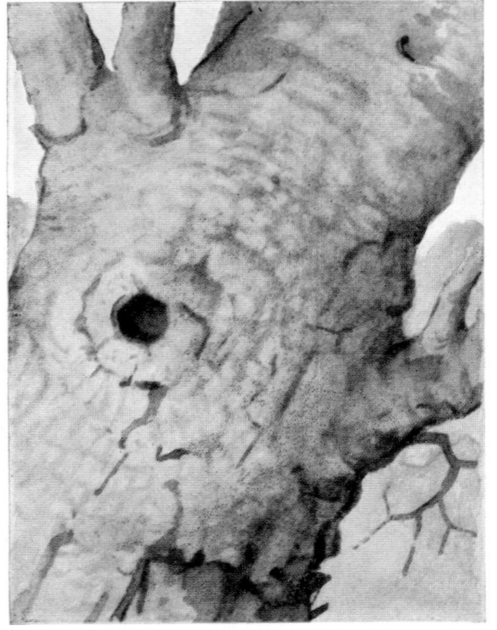

Nuthatch (see Plate XXXVIII.)

Tree-creeper (see Plate XXXVIII.)

THE TREE-CREEPER

THE Creeper's nest is begun in March or early in April; it is closely built, and the materials deftly woven together. Fine bark, roots, twigs, and mosses are used, with wool and some feathers on the inside. A favourite position is the crevice between the trunk of a tree and a piece of bark that stands off from it. Or he may build in a cleft in the trunk, or between two close branches, perhaps at the top of a pollard willow. And like the Tits, he often chooses the inside of a tree.

The Creeper lays from six to nine white eggs spotted with red or brown-red. They are difficult to distinguish from various other little red-speckled white eggs, such as those of some of the Tits. The young birds are very soon able to get about on the branches, and will escape from danger by creeping quickly up the tree away from the nest. Even when they are quite small the quills of the tail-feathers support them partially, and help them in their close little mouse-like movements.

THE GREAT TITMOUSE

SOME of the Titmice have an engaging way of building their nests in unexpected places. All sorts of quaint nooks have been chosen by the Great Tit and the Bluecap—the neck of a pump, the inside of a bottle or jar left out in a garden, a corner under the eaves of a house, or a letter-box. The nest of a Great Tit built in a letter-box, that is shown in the British Museum, must be familiar to hundreds of children. Then they quite frequently build in the old nests of Crows or other birds.

But the usual place for the nest of the Great Tit is a hole high up in a tree, or a hole in a wall. The young birds seem to have less discretion than many kinds of bird-babies, for very often, when walking along a country road bordered by an old wall, one is arrested by their loud peevish cries for food, that guide one directly to their home. The parent birds, however, are not less cautious than others, nor less devoted, and they do battle with bites and hisses when any harm is offered to their young ones.

Their nest is built of moss, wool, fine straws, and feathers, and lined with feathers. In a hole it is loosely made, but more tightly woven when it is in a more exposed position.

The eggs are white, speckled all over with pale red or brown-red. They vary very much in number, seven or eight being a usual nestful.

PLATES XI and XXXIX

THE COLE TITMOUSE

THE Cole Tit seems to prefer lower places for his nest than the Great Tit. The holes he chooses in trees are sometimes quite near the ground, and he may even find a place among the roots. He will enlarge a hole if necessary for his purpose by removing the soft wood from it. Again, the nest may be found in a hole in a wall or a bank; an old one made by a rat or mole is sometimes adopted. The materials used in building are moss, hair, wool, and feathers.

Two broods are reared in the season, the first family of six or eight young ones being hatched in May. The eggs are white, speckled and blotched with pale brownish red.

PLATES XII and XXXIX

THE BLUE TITMOUSE

THE Bluecap's nest may sometimes be found in the middle of a thick hedge or thorn-tree, but he usually elects to build in some snug covered corner, oftenest in a hole in a wall or tree. Blue Tits are bold, quarrelsome little people, and sometimes royal battles are waged by two couples who want one particularly suitable cranny for their home.

The nest is somewhat loosely and softly made, but of such materials—moss, wool, hair, and feathers—as cling together and make elaborate weaving unnecessary. It is softly lined with wool and feathers. In April the eggs are laid, seven, eight, or nine in number. They are of a delicate white, spotted with pale red more closely at the large end.

PLATES XII and XXXIX

THE LONG-TAILED TITMOUSE

THE Long-tailed Tit, or Bottle Tit, is one of the cleverest builders among British birds. His nest is quite an exquisite little mansion, and

PLATE XI

Great Tit (see Plate XXXIX.)

Cole Tit (see Plate XXXIX.)

PLATE XII

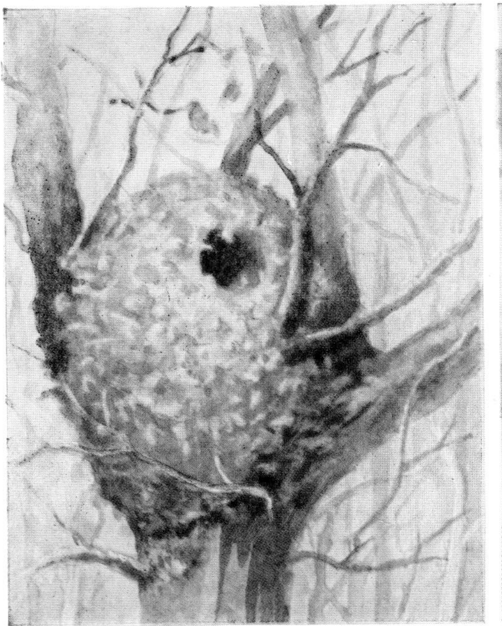

Long-tailed Tit (see Plate XXXIX.)

Blue Tit (see Plate XXXIX.)

takes a long time to make. It is different from the other Tits' nests in every way. To begin with, you must not look for it in a hole in a tree-stump, for this nest is placed in the branches of a tree or bush, often one that is covered with lichens. It is an oval ball, upright on one end. On one side near the top is a small hole, about an inch and a half wide, for the birds to get in and out by. The frame of the nest is made of moss, wool, and lichens worked together into a felt, the building of it being helped by cobwebs and gossamer. The outside is encrusted with flakes of lichens, and made to look very like the lichen-grey trunk near it.

And the inside is a miracle of work. It is difficult to think how these two tiny birds can collect in three weeks all the hundreds of feathers that go to make the softness of the lining. In some places the bird is called "Feather-poke," from the little bagful of feathers that is his nest. It is a biggish nest for the size of the birds; but when one thinks of the length of their tails, and the seven to ten, or even more, young ones whose home it is, each with a long tail, the wonder is that they can all get in.

Building begins in March, and the eggs are laid in the latter half of April. They are very round in shape, fragile little white things with very small red spots.

PLATES XIII and XXXIX

THE SWIFT

THE Swift builds a very slight nest. He hardly ever goes on the ground, but picks up any suitable materials he may find floating in the air, and of course these are of a very light and slender nature. Fine straws, scraps of wool, feathers, and cobwebs he collects, hardly enough substance, you would think, to build a nest with. But he glues them together with the sticky saliva that he discharges from his mouth, and so felts them into a little round, flat bed. This is made in some hole in a church-tower or in an old wall, or very often under the eaves of a cottage. And the birds often come back to the same corner for many years.

About the beginning of June the Swift lays two pure white eggs, the surface of which is somewhat rough. They are very long and narrow in form, more so than any other egg shown in these pictures. Unlike the Swallow and Martin that she resembles in so many ways, the Swift rears only one brood each summer.

THE SWALLOW

THE Swallow is a very familiar neighbour of our own, for he chooses to build his home near ours. Under the roof of a stable or barn, or in a sheltered corner in or about our chimney-tops his little mud walls are to be found. The nest is open on the top and shallow. It is formed of mud or clay, which the birds bring in their bills from the road or the banks of a river; and modelled while the material is damp and workable, it dries firm and strong. Inside this is a lining of fine straw and grasses, with a final bed of feathers on the top.

The four, five, or sometimes six eggs are like those of the Martin in form, being long and narrow. But their white surface is spotted all over with grey and brown. The first eggs are laid early in May, the second clutch about the beginning of July; and both broods can fly by the beginning of September, so they are strong and able for their long migration by the end of that month.

THE HOUSE-MARTIN

THE Martins are wonderful engineers, each in his own very characteristic way. The House-martin selects for his nest a position that is completely protected from above, and he builds so close to this ready-made roof that he has to leave an opening in the side to go in and out by. This site is generally found under the eaves of a house, in the upper corner of a window, or under a stone bridge. Sometimes large colonies of Martins build on the face of some cliff where they can find the necessary shelter. The nest is made of mud and clay, like the swallow's; but the shape is like half of a deep bowl stuck to the wall or cliff. The mud is rough on the outside, but the inside is smooth and softly lined with fine straw and feathers. Year after year one pair of Martins comes back to the same nest, just mending it if necessary and adding some fresh lining each summer.

Two broods of four or five young ones are reared each season. The eggs are pure white, rather long in shape, but not so long as the Swift's. The hen generally sits on the eggs, and rarely leaves the nest until the chicks are hatched, the cock in the meantime bringing food to her.

Swallow (see Plate XXXIX.)
Swift (see Plate XXXIX.)

PLATE XIV

House Martin (see Plate XXXIX.)

Sand Martin (see Plate XXXIX.)

PLATES XIV and XXXIX

THE SAND-MARTIN

IN a sandbank by a river or in a railway cutting or sand-pit, you may often see a lot of little round holes; watch them and you will see that the little mouse-brown Martins that are flying about keep going in and out. For the Sand-martin does not build up a home of clay like the House-martin, but digs out a hole in the sand in which to place his nest. You will find it impossible to see the nest, however, as these holes are entrances to long passages and lead two or three feet, or even more, into the sand. At the end they are widened out, and there the nest is formed of any kind of dry grasses very loosely laid together, and lined with feathers.

These tunnels slope up slightly so that rain cannot get in. The boring of them is all done with the bill, and must mean a great deal of very hard work for birds so small. When the hole is made the owners come back to it year after year.

In the middle of May the five or six eggs are laid, a second clutch following later. They are long in form and pure white, with very delicate, slightly transparent shells.

THE WATER-WAGTAIL OR PIED WAGTAIL

A GREAT wagging of long tails attracts attention when a family of five young Wagtails and two parents are going about together over your lawn, or in the meadow beside some open stream, and you cannot pass them by unnoticed. Is it simply the airy grace of their movements that makes Wagtails so charming? They are certainly delightful people.

Those half-dozen long tails all came out of a small nest built in a hole in a grassy bank; or it may have been in a hole in a wall, or under a furze-bush or in some crevice in a rock. The Water-wagtail uses fine materials in his building—fine grasses, fibrous roots, moss, wool, horse-hair, feathers.

Two clutches of eggs are laid in a summer, the first appearing about the end of April. They are of a pale blue-grey shade, spotted with grey and brown. Generally the markings are all over the egg, but occasionally they are found round the wider end only.

A pair of Wagtails very often comes back to the same haunt, building their nest in or about the same place year after year.

PLATES XV and XXXIX

THE GREY WAGTAIL

APPEARING as the Grey Wagtail does among grey rocks by some mountain stream or by the sea, something of surprise adds to our pleasure in seeing him. Just as the whin blossom seems to blaze forth in its greatest glory when a single bush surprises you among sombre surroundings, so this dainty creature, with his wonderful delicacy of form and colour, seems the more beautiful by contrast with the wildness of his haunts.

It is among grey rocks beside a river that he makes his nest, getting shelter under a rock or a low bush, or among grass and bents. Or he may build higher up, in some crevice in a rock under a protecting ledge, or in a hole in a bank. It is seldom more than a few feet away from water. In building, these birds use fine root fibres and straws and moss, with a careful lining of horse-hair, some wool and feathers.

Five or six eggs are laid. These vary in shades of greyish white, sometimes having a faint yellowish tinge. They are speckled or mottled all over with dull grey and brown. The first brood is to be seen out of the nest by the end of May or early in June.

PLATES XVI and XL

THE WHEATEAR

A PICTURE of the Wheatear's nest takes one's thoughts away to open meadows and grassy hillsides, stony commons and moors, airy and spacious. It is never among trees but in open country that the Wheatear becomes the familiar companion of one's rambles. He is always welcome and always pleasant to watch, attractive as he is both in form and in colour.

He comes to this country early in March and chooses for his summer home some hole in the ground or in a heap of stones, or a hole in a stone wall or in a peat-stack. Sometimes he adopts an old rabbit-burrow. There he makes his nest, loosely putting together dry bents and roots, wool and horse-hair, moss, feathers, or whatever suitable materials the neighbourhood affords. Building is begun in April or in the very beginning of May.

The eggs are five or six in number, pale greenish blue, without markings of any kind.

PLATES XVI and XL

THE STONECHAT

THE familiar, gay little figure of the Stonechat is very much in evidence in May, when he is surrounded by a family of five or six young ones,

PLATE XV

Pied Wagtail (see Plate XXXIX)

Grey Wagtail (see Plate XXXIX.)

PLATE XVI

Stonechat (see Plate XL.)
Wheatear (see Plate XL.)

just able to fly from branch to branch and all calling for attention. Their call is a soft, churring imitation of his. You will meet them about the whin and brambles on some open hillside or common. The parent birds always perch high enough to command a view of their surroundings, and are thus easily seen. They are generally shy and difficult to get near, but when the chicks are fledged they do not seem to resent one's approach, perhaps because they cannot help themselves, with all those little ones to protect.

Certainly the nest is very cleverly hidden away, and securely guarded from the possibility of human interference. It is placed on the ground under some low furze or straggling bramble, often in the very heart of some tangle far too dense and prickly to explore. Sometimes it may be found under a clump of heather or coarse grass. It is made of dry grass and moss, dry scraps of heather and roots, and lined with finer fibres and hair. It is a rather large, loosely built nest, and is begun early in April.

The eggs are pale bluish green in ground colour, with a circle of fine brown speckles round the large end.

PLATES XVII and XL

THE YELLOW-HAMMER

THE Yellow-hammer's is another nest that is to be found on the ground or close to it, in or under a furze-bush or a clump of grass. Very often it is in a hole in a bank, the entrance cunningly concealed behind tall grasses; or it may be hidden by the straggling branches of a hedge or bramble-thicket. It is made of dry grasses and roots, more neatly put together than in the Corn Bunting's nest; and it is lined with finer grasses and then with hair.

The Yellow-hammer begins building early in April, and the first nestful of eggs is laid in that month. These are four or five in number, of a dull, pale purplish colour, with spots and fine streaks and veinings of deep purple-red. Often a second brood is reared later in the summer.

PLATES XVII and XL

THE COMMON BUNTING

THE Common Bunting or Corn Bunting is not a bird of very great beauty or interest to us. He seems less gifted and attractive than most birds, which is perhaps the more fortunate for him, for he certainly must suffer less than many from the admiring attention of human kind. He has no particular grace or beauty of form, of colour or of song; and his nest, too, is rather uninteresting.

It is large but not deep, loosely made of hay and coarse grasses, and lined with finer grasses, root fibres, and some horse-hair. It is built late in April or in May, the eggs being laid so late as the very end of May. The nest is placed on the ground in a field of clover or corn, or raised in a tussock of grass in a bank under a hedge, or among some thick undergrowth.

The four or five eggs are dull grey, sometimes tinged with purple, and blotched and streaked with brownish grey or dark brownish purple. They vary considerably in colouring.

THE CORNCRAKE OR LANDRAIL

THE voice of the Corncrake you probably know very well. It is insistent and continuous. But his nest and eggs are a very different matter, difficult to find and get to know.

Always himself hidden away among tall grass or corn, in a clover field or among coarse rushes, he hides his nest there too, laying it in a furrow or an accidental hollow in the ground. It is made of dry grasses and stalks and leaves—a large, loose, uncovered nest.

The eggs may be any number from seven to twelve or even fourteen, but they are generally nine or ten. They are pale reddish brown or buff, with spots and large blotches of bright red-brown and greenish and purplish grey.

The Corncrake is a late summer visitor, and it is quite the end of May, or so late as June, before the eggs are laid. Very soon after the young birds are hatched they leave the nest, and learn to lie still and motionless to avoid detection on the approach of danger.

Common Bunting (see Plate XL.)
Yellow-hammer (see Plate XL.)

PLATE XVIII

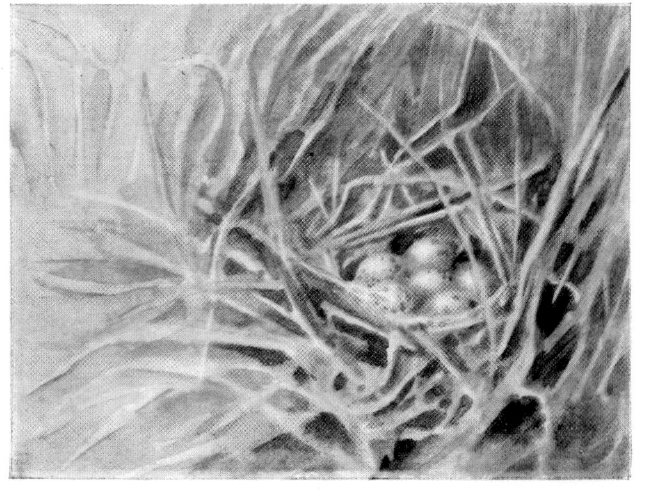

Skylark (see Plate XL.)
Corncrake (see Plate XL.)

THE SKYLARK

HOW often have you tried to find the Skylark's nest and carefully watched the spot from which the little creature has darted up heavenwards in an ecstasy of song? And having marked the very place you have gone straight to it to find no nest there at all. He never forgets that you or some one else may be there whom he does not wish to visit his home, and he always goes some distance in the grass before rising; nor does he come down directly to his nest.

It is in a slight hollow on the ground in a field of hay or corn, or under some clod or thick tuft of grass in a meadow. The Lark brings to his mate dry grasses and moss with which she builds the nest to her liking, and then fine grasses or horse-hair for the inside.

There in April she lays her four or five eggs. They are dull greenish white in ground-colour, spotted with dark brown all over, and at the larger end so densely that very little of the under-colour shows. When these young ones are fully fledged another family is reared, and perhaps even a third during the summer.

THE MEADOW-PIPIT

PERHAPS this is the nest you see oftener than any other, except those that are built in your garden. The Meadow-pipit is such a common bird everywhere; and nesting as he does in fields and open grassy meadows and hill-sides, you may so often see him leave his nest with nothing to prevent your marking its exact whereabouts. And of course the birds them-selves often give away their secret just by the anxiety they show when you go too near it.

It is a neat nest, laid in a hole on the ground under some firm tussock of grass or an over-hanging bank, or under a low bush, and it is often cleverly hidden. It is made of fine bents dexterously twisted together, and lined with fine grasses and hair, and sometimes root fibres and a little moss. It is somewhat large and deep, and often quite deeply set in the ground.

The eggs number from four to six, and are laid in April. They vary in ground-colour, and may be greyish or yellowish white, buff, pale brown, or a fairly dark brown. They are marked all over with close blots and speckles of dark brown. A later brood is often reared.

PLATES XIX and XL

THE ROCK-PIPIT

THE Rock-pipit is so like the Meadow-pipit in appearance and in voice that it is pleasantly interesting to find that his nest is quite different from that you have just seen. He is not quite so deft a builder as his cousin, and his nest is rather loosely contrived. He uses dried grasses and stems, mosses and the tough bents that grow near the seashore, and adds pieces of dry seaweed, which surely seems an unsympathetic sort of thing to make one's bed of. When the nest is lined some finer grasses and perhaps horsehair are used, but the lining is often dispensed with altogether.

The nest is carefully put out of sight in a hole or corner about the rocks of the seashore. Sometimes a clump of sea-pinks affords both shelter and a bright garden for his home among the greyness. The nest is also found among grass above the rocks, or concealed in the wrack left by some winter storm, high and dry above the summer tides.

Like those of the Meadow-lark, the eggs vary, but they are generally of a more or less greenish grey, mottled with dark grey and thickly spotted with reddish brown. In May the nest is filled with four or five eggs, and then again, when the first brood is fledged and self-supporting.

THE STARLING

THIS familiar frequenter of our chimney-tops builds most often in some hole about a house. A ruined tower will provide accommodation for many pairs, and suitable crevices are found under the eaves of houses or among well-grown ivy against the walls. Rocks and cliffs often afford good sites, and a very favourite position is a hole in a tree. Where the conditions are favourable, several nests are built close together, and the constant undercurrent of talk that goes on around them is amusing to listen to, reflecting as it does many of the natural sounds of the neighbourhood. For the Starling is an apt mimic, and if he lives where, for instance, the Curlew's note is often heard, his small imitation of it is so continual, that it might be taken to be his own natural song. The nest is large and rather loose and untidy. A great quantity of straws, twigs, roots, and moss go to the forming of it, and it is sometimes lined with hair or wool and a few feathers. It is built in April, and often the same nest is used for several years.

Two broods are reared in the season, and the four or five eggs are of a beautiful greenish blue. Starlings are devoted parents, and zealous in their care and attention to their young.

Rock-pipit (see Plate XL.)

Meadow-pipit (see Plate XL.)

PLATE XX

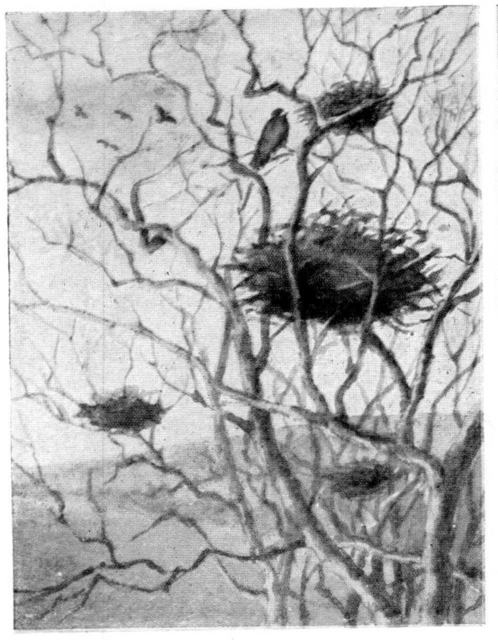

Rook (see Plate XLI.)

Starling (see Plate XL.)

PLATES XX and XLI

THE ROOK

THE sagacity and humour of its solemn inhabitants and the bustle of life that goes on in a rookery, make it a place of never-failing interest. Rooks build in colonies, many nests being placed near one another among the higher branches of some old well-grown trees, such as the oak or elm. These colonies have small beginnings, perhaps two or three pairs forming an offshoot from an older society. Then the young birds of each year add their nests to it until it is spread over many trees, and may number twenty, fifty, a hundred nests or more. These nests are used year after year, the birds coming occasionally during the winter to see how they are standing the rough weather.

In January or February they come to live in the rookery, and about the beginning of March—it is said in some places always on the first Sunday in March—the building of new nests or the repairing of old ones is begun. Very many sticks and twigs go to the making of one, and these are broken off the trees with much pulling and jerking, sometimes when they are specially tough, by the two birds together. The wide open cup is lined with straw, and is large for the size of the eggs that lie in it. About ten days of constant noise and bustle are occupied in building.

The Rooks lay four, five, or six bluish green eggs, spotted and blotched with greenish and dull brown.

THE JACKDAW

THE Jackdaw is most persistent in his building when he thinks he has found a good place for it. Many stories are told of Jackdaws dropping sticks and sticks into a hole in the hope of filling it up, where the hole is the top of a chimney or a small window on a belfry stair which they could never have time to fill, in spite of the enormous quantities of sticks they do collect. Or they will go on for days trying to make their sticks lie on a ledge that cannot hold them, a proceeding that is out of keeping with their solemn, grey-wigged appearance of wisdom.

Many old ruined castles have Jackdaws for their occupants every spring. They use holes about the old masonry, or in the face of cliffs, or under the roofs of houses. Or the hollow trunk of an old tree is a good place for a nest. It is filled up with sticks to a convenient height, and then dry leaves and straw are added, and a lining of wool and feathers and hair. Sometimes a hole in the ground, such as a rabbit's burrow, is made to serve.

The eggs are five or six, occasionally three or seven. They are laid about the beginning of May, and are of a pretty, pale blue-green, spotted with greenish and blackish brown.

PLATES XXI and XLI

THE MAGPIE

AMONG all the interesting ways of this engaging bird nothing is cleverer than the way he builds his nest. It is generally placed in the top of some tall tree, and the foundation is made of sticks cemented together with mud and clay. Smaller sticks and twigs are added, and the cup is softly lined with grasses and root fibres. It is then domed over, a hole being left at the side as a doorway; and for this the birds use twigs from thorn-bushes and leave the thorns sticking out in all directions. And they put thorns about the rest of the nest so that it becomes a splendidly fortified castle, and woe betide any enemy who tries to put in a hand or a paw for plunder!

Magpies pair for life, and generally come back to the same nest for several years in succession. Every year they add to it more sticks and more thorns, until the nest, which is large to begin with, becomes a huge structure.

Six or seven eggs are laid, of a pale greenish blue colour, blotched and spotted with dull grey and greenish brown.

PLATES XXII and XLI

THE JAY

THIS is another charming rogue that it is pleasant to meet in the woods. He does not, however, care to meet you. He will make no fuss about it, but quite quietly dodge to the other side of the trunk of the tree in which he is perching. As you walk round it he will quietly slip round too, his bright blue eye following your movements. He does not have friendly treatment from humankind, and has learnt to mistrust you.

So his nest is very carefully concealed in the thickest part of the wood. It is sometimes in a low bush, but generally fairly high up in the branches of a tree. It is an open nest with no roof, built of twigs and short sticks, with a lining of grasses, fibrous roots, and hair.

The eggs, which are laid about the beginning of May, vary in number from four to seven. They are dull greenish or yellowish grey, spotted closely all over with greenish or yellowish brown.

PLATE XXI

Jackdaw (see Plate XLI.)

Magpie (see Plate XLI.)

PLATE XXII

Wood Pigeon (see Plate XLI.)
Jay (see Plate XLI.)

PLATES XXII and XLI

THE WOOD-PIGEON OR RING-DOVE

THIS bird does no more than is necessary in the way of nest-building. He spends no time in finely finishing his home, or even in making the soft lining that so many birds like. It is a mere rough platform of sticks and twigs with smaller twigs on the top, and so loosely put together that the young ones can sometimes be seen from below, through the holes in the floor!

This shallow nest is placed on the branches of some high tree, generally at a considerable distance from the ground; or among thick ivy growing against a wall or cliff. It is begun some time in March, or even earlier in a mild season; and two broods are reared, and sometimes a third. The two eggs are white, with a smooth, glossy shell.

A point of interest about the Ring-dove is the curious way in which the young are fed. From the mouth of the parent the nestling drinks a liquid, called "pigeon's milk," that is prepared for it from half-digested food.

PLATES XXIII and XLI

THE BARN-OWL

THERE is one very curious thing about this bird's way of managing her family. In other bird families all the eggs in a nest are laid about the same time, and the young are hatched within a few hours of one another and are all young together; or else one brood is out and away before a new clutch of eggs is laid. It is not so with the Barn-owl; hers is something between those two plans. She lays two or three eggs, then waits for some days, perhaps till those are hatched, and lays two more; and then after a while perhaps another pair. So that her nest is an interesting one to see, sometimes containing birds nearly full fledged, newly hatched ones, and new eggs, all at the same time.

It really is hardly a nest at all—just a hole in an old tower or a corner in a belfry, a corner of a shelf in a barn, or, failing those, a hollow tree or a cleft in a rock. Often there is hardly even a lining for the hole, and at the best the nest is a loose collection of sticks with a little grass or straw in the centre. The eggs are of a round oval form, and their pure white shells are rough on the surface.

THE KESTREL

ABOUT the beginning of April the Kestrel decides upon some suitable spot in which to lay her eggs. She does not care to build a nest, and she must find a corner in which they will be protected, or at least lie safely. Very often the ledge of some high rock or cliff may be chosen, and she will scrape out a little hollow in the thin soil that lies there. Or perhaps she may find a hole in the cliff, or in some high tower, or in the trunk of a tree. Or the old nest of a Crow or Magpie in a wood may be made to do duty. The Kestrel can, however, build a nest when necessary. It is a rough collection of a few sticks and twigs with a little hay or wool added.

From four to six eggs are laid. They are short and broad, of a pale reddish or grey white, mottled over closely with bright rusty red-brown, sometimes so closely as to be almost covered with the darker shade. The young birds are fed entirely on insects at first, and only when they are nearly fledged do they begin to have a share of the field-mice on which their parents chiefly live.

THE SPARROW-HAWK

IT is of the nature of the Sparrow-hawk to adopt what doesn't belong to her. Small birds and nestlings are the things that tempt her oftenest, for they form the food on which she lives. But when it comes to nesting time, she will take possession without a scruple of the home built by other birds for their own use. More often she is found to take the old disused nest of a Magpie or a Crow or Ring-dove, which is merely renovated by her for her purpose. She may return to the same nest for several years in succession.

Oftener, however, Sparrow-hawks build a nest for themselves. They begin in April, and make it of sticks, lining it with twigs and occasionally a little dry grass. It is large, round, and shallow in form. The site chosen is generally in some high tree, the fir being a favourite, and it is well sheltered by foliage.

The eggs, four, five, or six in number, are of a round oval form. They are pale blue, heavily-blotted and marked, principally at the thicker end, with deep red-brown.

PLATE XXIII

Barn Owl (see Plate XLI.)

Kestrel (see Plate XLII.)

PLATE XXIV

Sparrow Hawk (see Plate XLII.)

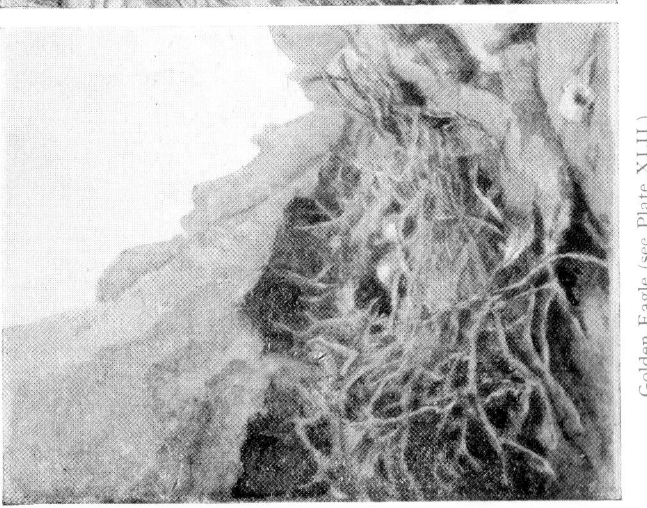

Golden Eagle (see Plate XLII.)

THE GOLDEN EAGLE

THE nest or eyrie of the Golden Eagle is formed on very high cliffs in desolate mountain fastnesses, on some ledge or in a rift in the rock. Of course it is a very big nest. And when you remember that the size and strength of this great bird are such that he can carry off a lamb in his talons, you will not be surprised to know that in building he uses whole big clumps of heather that you would find very hard to pull up, pulling with all your might. With these and large sticks the Eagle makes a broad, flat bed, adding some smaller materials, such as grass or fir twigs.

Built in such lonely, secure places, often where it is quite impossible for human beings to get near it, the eyrie is seldom disturbed, and the birds come back to it for years and years. They often add some more sticks to it in spring, so that it becomes in time a huge collection. Sometimes a pair will build at the top of some great high tree, but they generally prefer rocky mountains.

The two or three eggs are laid in the beginning of April and hatched in about a month. They are greyish white, spotted and clouded with light russet-brown and pale lavender. The young are covered at first with grey down.

PLATES XXV and XLIII

THE KINGFISHER

THIS brilliant little bird seems to know how the sunlight gleams on his feathers, and he is wise enough to go completely out of sight when he is engaged in the very private matter of nesting and tending his family. He selects a very safe place indeed, for he bores a tunnel two or three feet into the bank of the river where he fishes, and uses for his nest a chamber at the end of it. He does no further building. Discreetly, if he can find a passage already bored for him he does not make another; and sometimes a hole at the root of a tree serves, or more often, the old home of a Sand-martin. If a convenient place offers at a little distance from water, he will take it, but he generally lives beside his river.

When the birds frequent this home, they very soon accumulate there a quantity of stuff from the pellets they throw up of the indigestible bones of the fish they have swallowed. This substance makes a sort of carpet or lining for the nest, and as the same hole is used year after year, large quantities of it are sometimes found smoothed down to form a bed.

The eggs, which are laid in May, are pure white with a smooth, glossy surface, and very round in form. Their number varies from six to nine.

THE DIPPER

IMAGINE a muff made of soft green moss instead of fur; and imagine it set into a hole in the bank of a stream with the end of the muff showing, and you will see something like the Dipper's nest. The great ball of moss is down close to the water, and is kept green by the damp and coolness. The opening is a little slit in the middle, twice as broad as it is high. It is a difficult nest to find, even when it is visible, because it is like all the moss-covered stones that surround it. And it is often in some spot so protected by overhanging banks that you cannot see it at all except by wading in the water.

Dippers seem specially to love a waterfall, and often build in such a position that they must fly through falling water in going to and from the nest. The spray may continually wet the outside of their home, but the walls are thick, and the damp does not penetrate to the snug bed of dry leaves in the centre.

The shape of the nest, of course, varies somewhat according to the site in which it is placed, but it is always large for the size of the bird. It is always roofed, unless the position chosen affords a sufficient covering without. In many cases the same place is used year after year.

The Dipper begins building very early in the spring, and rears two or three broods. The pure white eggs are four, five, or six in number. They are narrow and long compared with those of the Dipper's nearest relatives, the Thrushes.

PLATES XXVI and XLIII

THE SANDPIPER

THE Sandpiper frequents the banks of lakes and rivers; not the smooth running rivers that wind among lush meadows and pasture lands, but in wilder, open country. He comes to us in April, and then his wild note may be heard near every highland stream and tarn, and his little restless figure seen hurrying about the banks or on the rocks amidstream.

Very soon after their arrival these birds begin to build. Their building is a very simple affair, and the nest owes more to the position chosen for it than to their small collection of dry leaves and grasses. It is placed in a slight hollow in a bank or in a tough clump of rushes; perhaps in a depression on the top of a little stretch of shingle out of reach of the water and close to overhanging grass; or even where some rock offers a suitable dip with a tuft of some plant for protection. It is always near water.

The four eggs are large for the size of the bird, and much pointed in shape. They are arranged in the nest with the smaller ends towards the centre. They are pale buff or grey in colour, spotted and splashed all over with pale grey and lighter and darker brown.

PLATE XXV

Kingfisher (see Plate XLIII.)

Dipper (see Plate XLIII.)

PLATE XXVI

Redshank (see Plate XLIII.)
Sandpiper (see Plate XLIII.)

PLATES XXVI and XLIII

THE REDSHANK

THE Redshank breeds in marshy places, by fens and lakes inland as well as near the sea. The position for the nest is chosen among heather or rushes or long grass; or sometimes a slight dip in the earth or peat may serve, generally where the surrounding or overhanging plants give shelter. A few dry bents loosely laid together, with a little finer grass for lining, is all the extent of the building. The four eggs are laid in May. They are greenish or reddish cream-colour, with irregular markings of light grey and dark red-brown, principally at the larger end. These marks vary considerably, and are much closer and more numerous in some cases than in others.

On danger threatening her young ones the Redshank's motherly devotion is shown in such a noisy fashion that one cannot but remark it. Perhaps she is no more careful and anxious than the bird that remains silently on her nest to the last moment and then slips off, quiet and inconspicuous; but she makes her wild, piercing cry pitifully unhappy, and flies round and round the intruder, sometimes threatening to dash down at him. Or she may limp away on the ground, trailing a wing as if it were broken, to divert his attention from her nestlings to herself.

PLATES XXVII and XLIII

THE RINGED PLOVER

THIS nimble little person is a very familiar figure about our sandy coasts. You may come quite close to him before you see him against the shingle that his colours so much resemble, and before he thinks of running off from you, the large intruder in his quiet haunts. He makes no noise, but silently runs along the ridge of broken shells and hard, dry seaweed that lies at the top of the tide, seeking his food.

Somewhere on that shingly bank, or on the sand at the head of the bay, below where the grass begins, is a slight hollow that he has selected for his nest. He does no building whatever; only sometimes a few broken shells are collected in the sandy hollow, perhaps in order that the eggs may show less against their parti-coloured setting.

The colour of the eggs, however, is such that they are not readily seen in the positions the bird chooses for them. They vary in shades of sand- and stone-colour, and are covered with small speckles of grey and black. They are pear-shaped, and lie with their points together. In May the first clutch of four is laid, and often a second brood follows. The newly-hatched birds, with their prodigiously long legs and cunning little broad heads, are especially attractive, even among bird-babies.

PLATES XXVII and XLIII

THE MOORHEN

THE thick flags and sedges by the margin of a lake or beside a river flowing slowly through grassy meadows, afford the Water Hen the concealment she likes for her large nest. The nest may lie actually in the water or just beside it. Sometimes the stump of a tree supports it several feet from the surface, or the branch of an overhanging willow holds it, touched by the water and moved with its motion.

The nest is made of flags, and the grass and stems of reeds, and dry leaves. It is open above, and on leaving it the Moorhen lays rushes over it to hide it, and perhaps to keep the eggs warm.

A clutch of eggs may consist of any number from six to ten or even more. As the first brood, hatched in May, is only about a fortnight old when the hen begins to lay the second clutch, you will not be surprised that the parents often hastily build a second nest to hold some of the family. By the time the second lot of chicks are out the first are able to help to feed them. And they lend their aid, too, in building further accommodation, as still another family is immediately forthcoming.

The eggs are particularly pretty ones; they are of a pale buff colour, delicately speckled with red-brown and soft grey.

PLATES XXVIII and XLIV

THE PHEASANT

PHEASANTS were brought to this country from the East hundreds of years ago, and if they were left entirely to fend for themselves they would not be strong enough to stand the rigour of our winter climate, and would gradually decrease in number and probably die out altogether. But they are fed and sheltered in winter, and so, although many thousands are killed every year by the sportsman's gun, their numbers are kept up.

They live about woods and plantations, and the hen lays her eggs on the ground, among dry coarse grass or under a hedge. At the most, a few leaves or straws are collected by way of a nest.

The eggs are of a pale brown-green without spots, and vary in number from six to thirteen. The cock leaves the hen when the eggs are laid, and she has to bring up the family alone. As he has several mates, each with a large nestful of eggs, he could not very well help them all. The young birds very soon learn to find food for themselves.

PLATE XXVII

Moorhen (see Plate XLIII.)

Ringed Plover (see Plate XLIII.)

PLATE XXVIII

Grouse (see Plate XLIV.)
Pheasant (see Plate XLIV.)

THE GROUSE

THE Grouse, the only native of Great Britain that belongs to Great Britain alone, is a bird of the heather and moorland. He always lives on high land where the hillside is dry and heather-clad. The birds pair early in the year and the nest is formed on the ground, sheltered on all sides by heather. A slight hollow is scraped out, and dry bents or scraps of heather are used to line it.

In March or April the hen lays her eggs, and she alone sits on them. They are most often eight or nine, but may be any number from five to twelve or even more. Their colour is light buff, thickly spotted and splashed with very dark red-brown.

Between three or four weeks later the eggs are hatched, and both birds feed and tend the family. They are very careful parents, and on the approach of danger they steal away through the heather to some distance from the young ones before they rise. Or they will pretend to be hurt, and drag themselves off along the ground, trying to draw the enemy away from their chicks.

THE PARTRIDGE

THE Partridge builds little, and the safety and comfort of her nest depend very much on the position chosen for it. The birds are very deliberate and careful in selecting a safe place. It is often in a field of growing corn or hay, among clover or coarse grass or weeds, under the protection of a hedge, or under low bushes and undergrowth. A slight hollow is scratched in the ground or the grass is trodden down, and the dip so made is lined with some dry grass and leaves.

The number of the eggs varies very much, and may be anything from six to eighteen or twenty or even more. They are laid about the beginning of May, and are of a uniform olive-brown, somewhat long and pointed in form. Both birds attend most devotedly to the nestlings, and the ruse of feigning to be hurt, that is used by many anxious bird-parents to draw off an enemy, is often adopted by the Partridge.

PLATES XXIX and XLIV

THE LAPWING OR PEEWIT

THE Peewit is an anxious parent, and in his concern lest you should interfere with his domestic affairs, he forces himself and them on your notice by his wild, plaintive cry whenever you come near the vicinity of his home. It is a very familiar cry to any one whose country walks lead him through open places, fields and commons and moors. The insistent "Pees-weep" becomes louder and angrier as you come near his nest, while the birds circle round above your head, sometimes dashing down towards you. Then one will feign to have a broken wing, and dragging it on the ground, will run away, hoping you may follow and that he may thus lead you away from his eggs or young.

No nest is built, but some scraps of grass or rushes are loosely collected in a hollow on the ground. The site is very often chosen on wet or marshy ground, and then the bed is on some little mound or hillock so that the eggs do not lie in water.

The eggs, four in number, are not easy to see, even if you are close upon them, although they lie comparatively unsheltered. Their colour, dull-greenish or brownish buff, splashed and spotted all over with darkest brown, is very inconspicuous among the grass or heather.

PLATES XXX and XLV

THE CURLEW

IT is difficult to get to know much about the Curlew and difficult to find his nest. A wild voice comes to you out of the distance, full of strange beauty, and that is all most of you know of the bird, and the bird prefers that you should know no more. He never lets you come near him, and his home is made on lonely, desolate moors high on the hills, where you are least likely to find him. And another safeguard is that it is very often placed on marshy ground, on some small dry patch on the flat parts of the moors where water lies. Bog-myrtle and cotton-grass are often its protection. Or it may lie concealed among rushes or bents or under a clump of heather. The curlew makes very little nest, simply lining with a few dry grasses some slight hollow in the ground.

There, in April or May, she lays four large pear-shaped eggs, arranging them to lie with their narrow ends towards one another. They are dull olive-green or greenish buff, marked with blotches of dark brown and green or purplish grey. The colouring varies considerably. The young birds run about almost as soon as they are hatched, and know at once to lie flat under cover on a warning call from their parents.

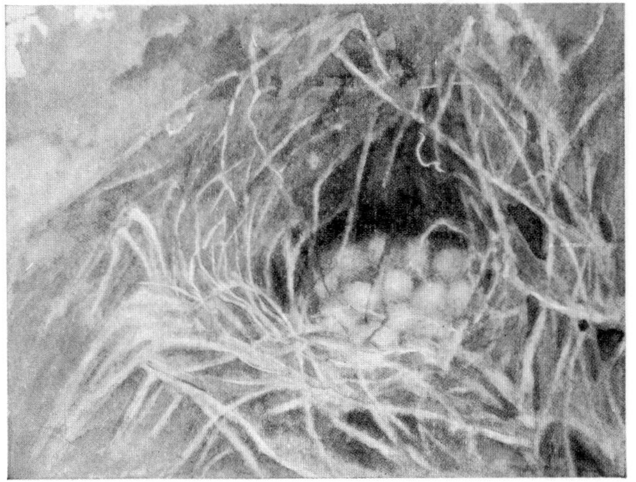

Lapwing (see Plate XLIV.)
Partridge (see Plate XLIV.)

PLATE XXX

Curlew (see Plate XLV.)
Snipe (see Plate XLV.)

THE SNIPE

THE Snipe must have soft mud or bogs in which to find his food, so his nest is never to be sought for far from water or wet ground. By the sides of ponds, rivers or marshes it is hidden among the rushes, or in a tuft of coarse grass. Or by some tarn high up among the hills you may find it sheltered under the heather. It is merely a hollow in the ground lined slightly with dry grass or leaves or scraps of heather. It is generally formed during the latter part of April.

The four eggs are pale yellowish or olive-green, blotched, chiefly at the larger end, with grey and lighter and darker brown. They are very large for the size of the bird, and that she may the better cover them in the nest, they lie with their narrow pointed ends in the centre. The hen alone sits on the eggs, while the cock spends much of his time flying round and round above her, "drumming." But when the young leave the nest, as they do immediately they are hatched, both the old birds care for them.

THE HERON

A HERONRY is the name given to the home of a colony of Herons, and it is a strange and interesting place. The nests are built at the very tops of trees in a wood. If some widely spreading kind of tree is chosen, then many nests may be built on the branches of one. Often it is in a pine-wood, and each of a group of trees is crowned with a nest. This is a curious great rough platform of large sticks, sticks for the most part as thick as the bird's own leg. It has no particular shape, but is simply a flat place large enough to support the three or four eggs, and covered on the top with a soft layer of roots and dry grass and rushes.

On each of these nests you may see several tall young Herons standing up eagerly watching for the return of their parents with food. And every old bird coming to the Heronry is greeted with a chorus of harsh squawks from the young of the whole colony.

Often, too, later in the season, when there is no such pressing business to be done as the feeding of young ones, you may see many birds standing, solemn and motionless, each on the very top of a tree. The same Heronry is used year after year if the birds are undisturbed.

The eggs are of a pale bluish green colour without markings. Two broods are reared, and as a rule the first eggs are laid in March, but in a mild season they may be laid even so early as January.

PLATES XXXI and XLV

THE WILD DUCK

THE home of the Wild Duck is to be found close to a lake or pond, or a river with quiet pools, just far enough off to ensure a dry spot to build on. For the nest is on the ground among grass or bents or under low sheltering vegetation of some sort. Sometimes it may be on marshy ground, but the stiff rushes among which it is placed keep it from lying low enough to be damp. It is a small nest for the size of the bird and for the number of her family, regularly built of bents, stems, and grasses; its lining is a very thick warm one of down.

Building commences about the end of March or the beginning of April. As soon as the Duck has begun to sit on her eggs, the Drake's moulting season arrives and he leaves her. So when she goes off to feed and there is no one else to care for the eggs, she covers them over with down to keep them warm in her absence. When the young ones are hatched and have to be fed too, that difficulty is simplified, for she takes them to the water at once, and they swim around her while she finds their food. As there are about ten of them, however, it must be no light task.

The eggs are palest green, with a smooth surface.

THE CORMORANT

THIS curious creature likes rocky coasts, and builds his nest on a ledge of a high cliff or rocky island. Many pairs of Cormorants build close together and come back to the same nesting-place every year. The nest is a large heap of sticks and sea-weed, often as much as two feet high, and finished on the top with some coarse grass.

Four to six eggs are laid in April, or more often in May. They are pale blue-green, covered over with a thick coat of white chalk. In four weeks the young birds come out, and funny-looking little sweeps they are! Many birds are born with a pretty, fluffy coat of down, but the baby-Cormorant has no covering on his queer little blue-black body. And when he grows a coat it is a black woolly one that is just like soot when it begins to appear.

Another strange thing about this ugly little family is the way in which it is fed. The parents carry in their gullets food they have swallowed. Then when the mother arrives with a pouchful, she bends with open mouth over the young one, and he puts his head right inside her mouth and drinks.

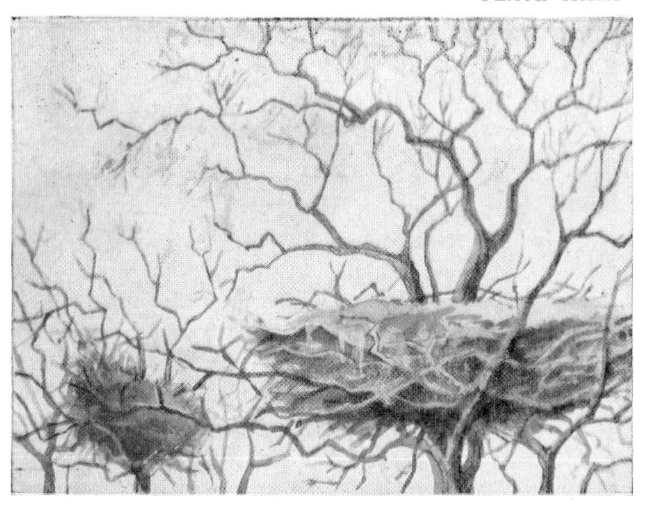

Heron (see Plate XLIV.)
Wild Duck (see Plate XLV.)

PLATE XXXII

Oystercatcher (see Plate XLVII.)
Cormorant (see Plate XLV.)

THE OYSTER-CATCHER

THE Oyster-catcher lives about the shore where there are low rocks, shingle, and sandy bays. And there, above high-water mark, she finds a slight dip or hollow, either on the bare rock or among the tough bents or grass above it, for her nursery. Or she may scrape a hollow in the sand to suit her, or sometimes she nests on the pebbly bank of a river. The Oyster-catcher does not build a nest, but merely collects in this little dip some broken white shells. They are a curious thing to make a bed of, and surely cannot be chosen like the soft linings of other nests with a view to the comfort of the nestlings. Perhaps it is in order that the eggs may show less against a background of broken colour; or perhaps that by being raised off the rock they may run no risk of lying in water.

The eggs are generally three, sometimes four in number. They are dark cream-colour or pale buff, spotted and streaked with blackish-brown and a light red-brown or grey

The Oyster-catcher is very noisily angry if you go near his nest, and the owners of a few nests together make a clamour of protest that is almost deafening.

PLATES XXXIII and XLVI

THE COMMON GULL

THE Common Sea-gull is common in summer only in the northern parts of this island. It does not breed anywhere round the English coast. In Scotland large colonies are to be found nest-building in April. They frequent inland lochs as well as the sea-coast. The nests are built either on the ledges of steep cliffs or any rocky part of the coast; or they may lie up on the moors, far from rocks; and the small islands in either fresh-water or sea lochs are favourite spots, and become the homes of large communities. Sometimes many pairs nest close together; again, two or three pairs, or even a single pair alone.

The nest is a large one, made of heather, dry seaweed, or grasses. The three eggs are laid early in May. In colour they vary from a pale yellowish white to dark olive-brown, blotched and spotted with dark brown, grey and black.

PLATES XXXIII and XLVI

THE BLACK-BACKED GULL

OF the two kinds of Black-backed Gulls that frequent our shores the Lesser is by far the commoner, and it breeds in suitable places all round the coast. In the spring these birds collect in large numbers and many nests are formed side by side, so close together that on some of their favourite islands you must step with caution to avoid damaging them or their contents. Your being there at all the birds much resent, and they make a wild clamour overhead so long as you remain near.

On islands in the sea there are often vast colonies of them, and they also nest in some inland places, on moors, or beside inland lakes or on islands in them. The nests vary very much. Sometimes a small quantity of grass and dry seaweed serves; sometimes it is a very large collection.

The eggs are two or three in number, and vary in all shades of greenish brown and stone-colour, and pale greens and blues. They are thickly blotched and spotted with darkest brown and grey.

As with all the Gulls, the young of the Black-backed Gull do not have the colours of the old birds till they are about three years old. Until then the back is not black, but is beautifully marked with soft brown and white.

PLATES XXXIV and XLVI

THE BLACK-HEADED GULL

THE Black-headed Gull is more generally familiar than the Common Gull, and familiar, too, not only to those who live by the sea, for he spreads all over the country, and the breeding season brings him inland. This Gull does not build by the sea, but comes about fens and bogs and lakes for his spring quarters.

The nest is made on an island in a marsh or broad, where it may be placed right on the ground or in a clump of grass; or else it may be in the marsh itself, when it is raised about a foot above the surface of the water among strong reeds and rushes. It is formed of grass and scraps of sedges and reeds, lined with finer grasses, and is loosely built and shallow in form.

The three or four eggs may be palest blue or green, buff or a darker brown; and the markings of black and dark brown vary very much in number.

Enormous numbers of these birds nest close together, and come back to the same locality year after year. An intruder in one of their colonies is greeted with very noisy expostulation. The birds fly round and round him, occasionally darting down as if to strike him, and protesting with their loud, laughing cries. When the young are newly hatched and still tiny balls of mottled down, they leave the nest and go to the water.

Black-backed Gull (see Plate XLVI.)

Common Gull (see Plate XLVI.)

PLATE XXXIV

Black-headed Gull (see Plate XLVI.)

Gannet (see Plate XLVII.)

Shearwater (see Plate XLVII.)
Tern (see Plate XLVII.)

PLATE XXXVI

Guillemot (see Plate XLVIII.)

Puffin (see Plate XLVIII.)

PLATES XXXIV and XLVII

THE GANNET

SEEN flying out at sea the Gannet is a beautiful bird. The strength of his flight and the power and swiftness with which he dives are always delightful to watch. And it is something of a disappointment to see him for the first time at close quarters. His white coat proves to be yellowish, and his curious black-circled eye has a sinister look. On his nest the Gannet is interesting, but he is not attractive.

Many hundreds of these birds breed together, taking possession of some high rocky island in the sea. On Lundy Island, Ailsa Craig, the Bass Rock, almost every ledge that gives room for it bears a nest. And in the busiest time, when the young birds are being fed and the old ones are constantly coming and going, there is quarrelling among them all day long, merely for standing room.

The nests are very simple collections of seaweed and a few sticks, with some grass on the top. The grass is not enough to keep the white egg off the seaweed, and it soon gets stained and dirty. Under a rough cover of white chalk the egg is pale greenish blue. The young bird is hatched with no coat on, but after the first week is covered with grey down. When it is fledged it wears dark colours, and it has not the full adult plumage until it is four years old.

THE TERN

THE Tern or Sea-swallow is a summer visitor, and comes to these shores about the middle or end of April. A group of several pairs generally breed together on some low island in a sheltered arm of the sea; and they are sometimes to be found nesting beside other kinds of sea-birds. The nest is a mere hollow in the sand above high-water line on bare rock, or most often among pebbles or shingle. Often a few scraps of fine dry grass and roots are arranged in it, but just enough to keep the eggs off the stones.

The colouring of the eggs, which varies to pale blues and greens, but is most often pale buff or grey stone-colour, mottled over with dark brown and black, makes them difficult to see against such a background. And as in the case of some other birds, who lie during their helpless infancy in exposed places, the same protective colouring is repeated in the down of the young chicks. They, too, are yellowish grey or stone-colour, mottled with darker brown.

The eggs, which are two or three in number, are laid about the beginning of June, and hatched between two and three weeks later.

THE SHEARWATER

THE Shearwater is a sea-bird only. He does not come about the shore, and you can see him best from a boat, walking on the water or shearing the wave-crests with his wings in his graceful, gliding flight. Only in spring does he come to land, and then it is to dig a burrow to be his nest. This is done in sandy or peaty soil at the top of some sea-cliff or headland, or on the highest grassy part of an island out at sea. Sometimes some lining of dry grasses and ferns is put at the end of the tunnel; sometimes it is unlined, and the one smooth white egg is laid on the bare peat.

It is laid in June. Being the only child of most devoted parents the young bird is well cared for, and is in no hurry to turn out and fend for himself. He stays in the nest for some time after he is fully fledged. During the nesting season the Shearwaters stay underground most of the day, and do all their fishing by night. In August, when the young one is ready, they all go out to sea again.

THE GUILLEMOT

THIS is another bird that leaves the water only to lay her egg and to tend her young one. For this business hundreds and thousands of birds collect together on a rocky headland or some island stack of rocks. And on every ledge on the face of the cliff, and all over the top of the rocks lie the eggs, so close together as to give only room for each mother to attend to her own. If the Guillemot chose to sit on her egg in the usual way, she could not lay it on such very narrow ledges as she does select, for they would not give her room. But she stands over it, holding it between her legs and under the feathers of her tail to keep it warm. So you see rows and rows of birds standing up like sentinels against the cliff, bowing and nodding quaintly to one another and all the world, instead of lying down as in gulleries and other breeding-stations.

And lying exposed on those narrow ledges, you wonder why the eggs are not blown off. But they are so shaped and balanced, with one end thick and the other very long and pointed, that the wind merely turns them round on their own centres and cannot roll them off.

They are very large for the size of the bird, and of any and every colour. White, cream, buff, pale or deep blue, palest green or a dark

1. Missel-Thrush (I.) 2. Song-Thrush (I.) 3. Blackbird (II.)
4. House-Sparrow (II.) 5. Chaffinch (III.) 6. Greenfinch (III.)
7. Bullfinch (IV.) 8. Goldfinch (IV.) 9. Linnet (V.)
10. Whitethroat (V.)

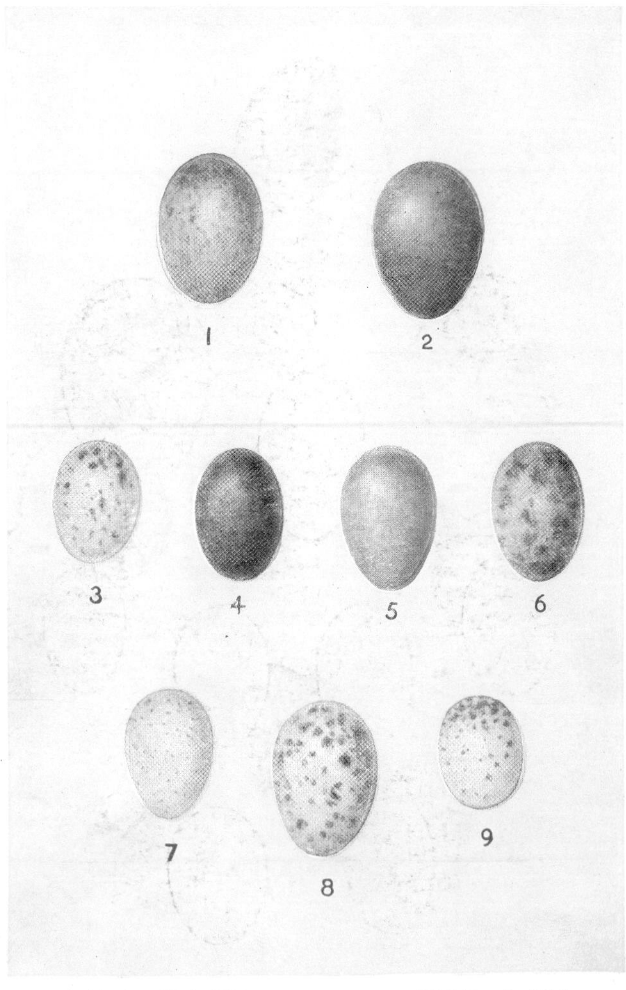

1. Robin (see Plate VI.)
2. Nightingale (VI.)
3. Willow-Warbler (VII.)
4. Sedge-Warbler (VII.)
5. Hedge-Sparrow (VIII.)
6. Flycatcher (VIII.)
7. Wren (IX.)
8. Nuthatch (X.)
9. Tree-creeper (X.)

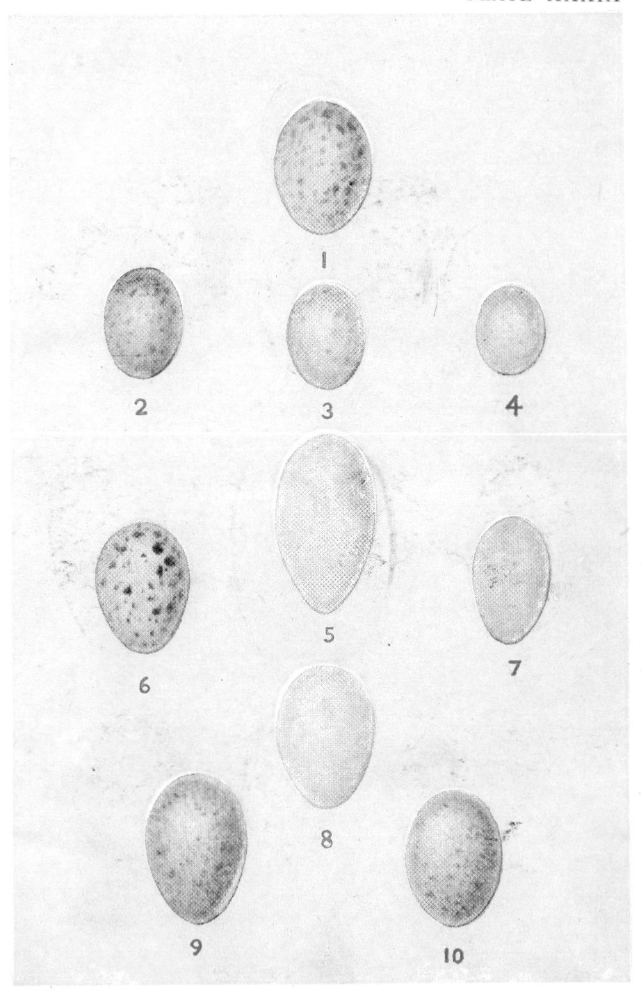

1. Great Tit (see Plate XI.) 2. Cole Tit (XI.) 3. Blue Tit (XII.)
4. Long-tailed Tit (XII.) 5. Swift (XIII.) 6. Swallow (XIII.)
7. Sand Martin (XIV.) 8. House Martin (XIV.)
9. Pied Wagtail (XV.) 10. Grey Wagtail (XV.)

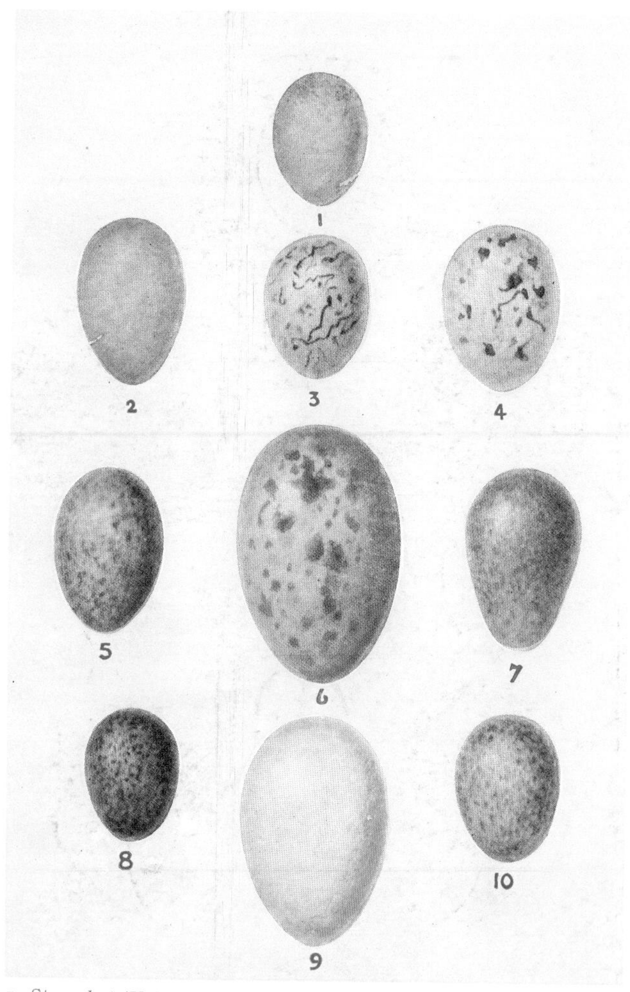

1. Stonechat (XVI.) 2. Wheatear (XVI.) 3. Yellow-hammer (XVII.)
4. Common Bunting (XVII.)
5. Cuckoo (IX.)
6. Corncrake (XVIII.)
7. Skylark (XVIII.)
8. Meadow-pipit (XIX.) 9. Starling (XX.) 10. Rock-pipit (XIX.)

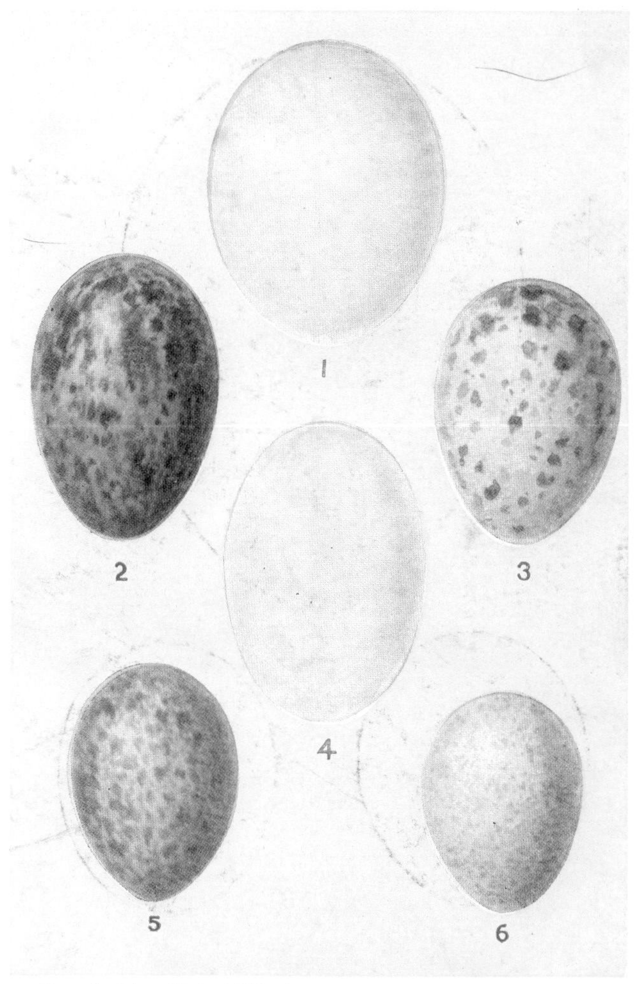

1. Barn Owl (see Plate XXIII.)
2. Rook (see Plate XX.)
3. Jackdaw (see Plate XXI.)
4. Wood Pigeon (see Plate XXII.)
5. Magpie (see Plate XXI.)
6. Jay (see Plate XXII.)

PLATE XLII

1. Golden Eagle (see Plate XXIV.) 2. Kestrel (see Plate XXIII.) 3. Sparrow Hawk (see Plate XXIV.)

1. Moorhen (see Plate XXVII.)
2. Dipper (XXV.)
3. Ringed Plover (XXVII.)
4. Kingfisher (XXV.)
5. Sandpiper (XXVI.)
6. Redshank (XXVI.)

PLATE XLIV

1. Lapwing (see Plate XXIX.) 2. Heron (XXXI.)
3. Pheasant (XXVIII.) 4. Grouse (XXVIII.) 5. Partridge (XXIX.)

1. Curlew (see Plate XXX.)
2. Wild Duck (see Plate XXXI.)
3. Cormorant (see Plate XXXII.)
4. Snipe (see Plate XXX.)

PLATE XLVI

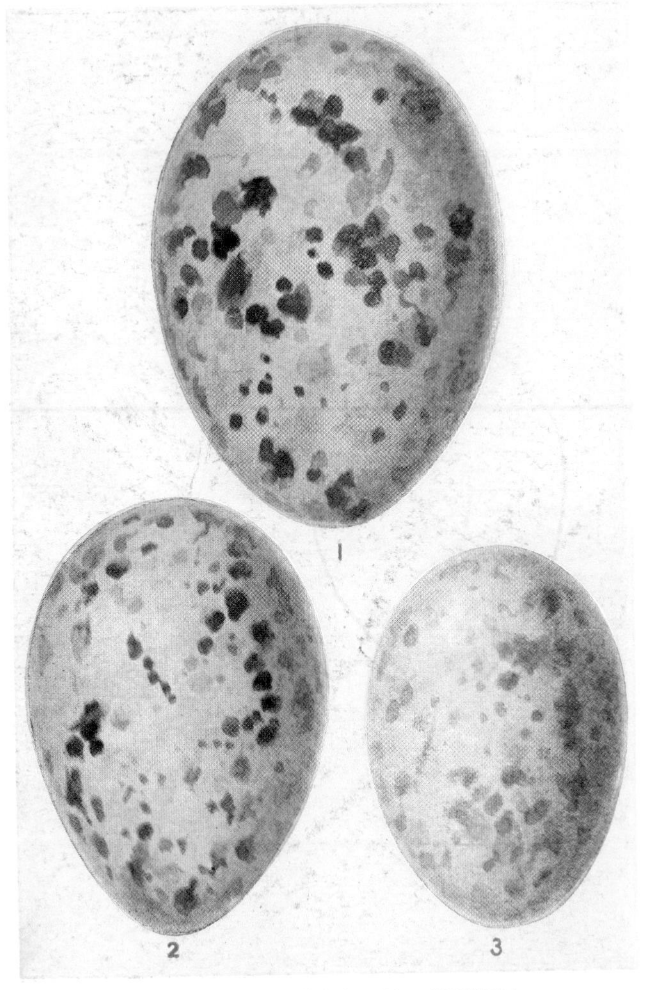

1. Black-backed Gull (see Plate XXXIII.)
2. Common Gull (see Plate XXXIII.)
3. Black-headed Gull (see Plate XXXIV.)

1. Gannet (see Plate XXXIV.)
2. Shearwater (see Plate XXXV.)
3. Oystercatcher (see Plate XXXII.)
4. Tern (see Plate XXXV.)

PLATE XLVIII

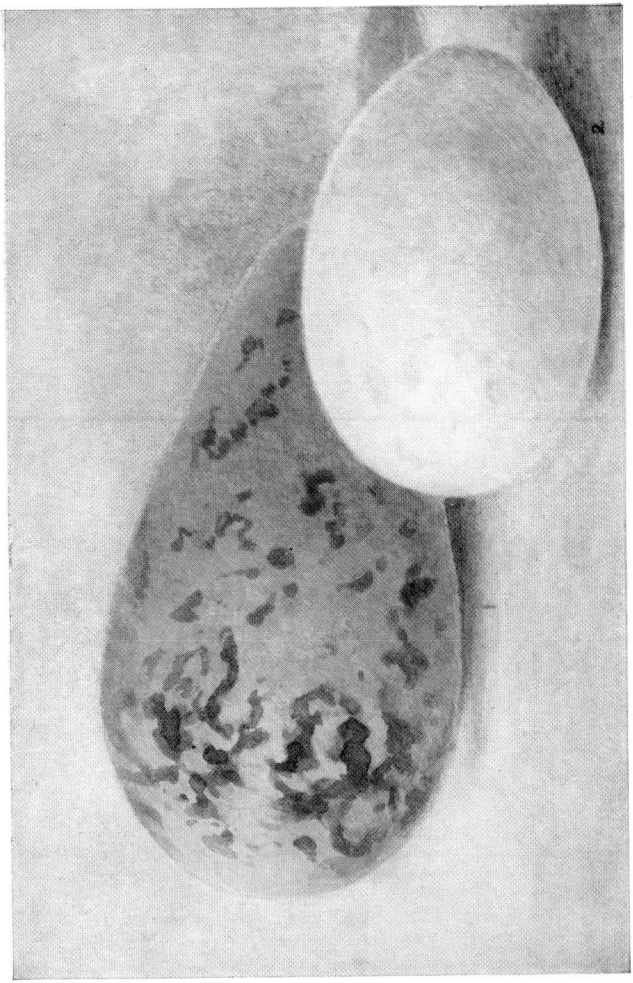

1. Guillemot (see Plate XXXVI.)   2. Puffin (see Plate XXXVI.)

sea-green, yellow or brown, they may be; and there the variety does not end, for they are streaked and blotted in every sort of fashion with dark colours and black.

PLATES XXXVI and XLVIII

THE PUFFIN

THE Puffin likes a hole to hide his egg in. A favourite one is a rabbit-hole, and he has no scruples about turning out the owner when he finds such a place to suit his purposes. A hole or crevice in a rock is often used, or he burrows out for himself a tunnel in sandy earth or peat; and when he is thus engaged the bird is often so intent that he will allow himself to be taken in the hand. And the hen too, while sitting, is very fearless, and allows herself to be lifted rather than leave her charge. Both birds defend the nest by biting, which they do strongly with their heavy beaks.

Their cave is made two or three feet long, and at the end of it the one egg is laid in June. It is pale grey, blotted a little with grey and soft brown.

The young bird is fed with fish which the parents bring to it several at a time, with the tails hanging out from both sides of their bills.

At the end of August the birds leave again for the open sea.

WHERE TO FIND THE NESTS AND EGGS

ABOUT HOUSES, GARDENS, OR SHRUBBERIES

Missel-thrush	Bullfinch	Hedge-sparrow	Starling
Song-thrush	Goldfinch	Flycatcher	Swallow
Blackbird	Whitethroat	Wren	House-martin
House-sparrow	Redbreast	Nuthatch	Swift
Chaffinch	Nightingale	The Titmice	
Greenfinch	Willow-wren	Pied Wagtail	

IN FIELDS OR HEDGEROWS

(WITH THEIR TREES)

Missel-thrush	Redbreast	Yellow-hammer	Jackdaw
Song-thrush	Linnet	Corncrake	Barn-owl
Blackbird	Hedge-sparrow	Meadow-pipit	Magpie
House-sparrow	Flycatcher	Skylark	Wood-pigeon
Chaffinch	Wren	Starling	Pheasant
Greenfinch	Corn Bunting	Rook	Partridge
Whitethroat			

ON MEADOWS OR COMMONS

Goldfinch	Wheatear	Yellow-hammer	Rook
Linnet	Stonechat	Skylark	Pheasant
Flycatcher	Corncrake	Meadow-pipit	Partridge
Wren	Corn Bunting	Starling	Peewit
Pied Wagtail			

IN THE WOODS

Redbreast	Nuthatch	Jay	Kestrel
Nightingale	Tree-creeper	Wood-pigeon	Pheasant
Willow-wren	The Tits	Barn-owl	Heron
Wren	Magpie	Sparrow-hawk	

ON MOOR OR MOUNTAIN SIDE

Wren	Stonechat	Grouse	Curlew
Wheatear	Meadow-pipit	Peewit	Snipe

BY LAKE OR RIVER

Sedge-warbler	Grey Wagtail	Sandpiper	Snipe
Snipe	Kingfisher	Redshank	Wild Duck
Sand-martin	Dipper	Moorhen	Sea-gulls

BY THE SEASHORE

Rock-pipit	Ringed Plover	Black-backed Gull	Puffin
Redshank	Oyster-catcher	Tern	

ABOUT CLIFFS OR ROCKS

Starling	House-martin	Barn-owl	Gannet
Jackdaw	Kestrel	Cormorant	Shearwater
Swift	Golden Eagle	Common Gull	Guillemot

INDEX

PRINTED IN GREAT BRITAIN AT
THE PRESS OF THE PUBLISHERS